Introduction

When I was choosing the poems to make up this collection, I wanted to make sure that there would be poems of different types and different moods – poems to make you laugh, poems to make you think and poems which would tug at your emotions.

Every person who reads this collection will have their own favourites – perhaps because a poem reminds you of a particular event, place, person or time in your own life. For that is what writers are able to do … they imagine or experience something, changing and shaping it as they create a poem which then reaches out to you, the reader. As you read the words of any of these poems, you will be sharing an experience or an idea with the poet who wrote it, for a poem is like a window into a writer's mind and emotions.

All the writers of the poetry in this collection are women. You may have read some of their poetry or stories before, but the poems in this book are all new.

Wendy Body

CONTENTS

THROUGH A
WINDOW

poems selected
by Wendy Body

LONGMAN

This book is part of
THE LONGMAN BOOK PROJECT

General Editor Sue Palmer
Fiction Editor Wendy Body
Non-fiction Editor Bobbie Neate

ACKNOWLEDGEMENTS

We are grateful to the following copyright holders for permission to reproduce
previously unpublished poems.

Moria Andrew for *Poems aren't all that difficult, Night* and *Nursery rhyme 1992*;
Carolyn Askar for *Reasons for writing*; Debjani Chatterjee for *The Yeti*;
Wendy Cope for *School reports* and *Where do you get your ideas from?*;
Sue Cowling for *Pete's leg* and *No ball games*; Helen Dunmore for *Pearlie Mountblossom*
and *Light as a leaf*; Heather Eyles for *A Spanish soldier first sees Tenochtitlan*
and *A captured warrior waits to be sacrificed*; Katherine Gallagher for *Wheels-song,
Books* and *Sylvester Snake*; Susan Gates for *Fair game* and *All the way to Africa*;
Adèle Geras for *Seaside* and *A poem about housework*; Sophie Hannah for *Rocky* and *Gloves*;
Una Leavy for *Bells* and *Go-cart*; Primrose Lockwood for *Windows*; Gerda Mayer for
The mermaids in the sea are, Stock still and *Malham Tarn Field Centre; Yorkshire 1992*;
Michaela Morgan for *I don't cry, Love hearts, Blake's Tyger-revisited* and *Family meals*;
Judith Nicholls for *Jack's tale*; Sue Stewart for *Shadow, February* and *There's a surprise*.

The publishers are grateful to the following for permission to reproduce the following photos:

Eye Abiquitos, pages 16, 23, 29, 53; Sally and Richard Greenhill, pages 33;
The Image Bank, pages 28, 49; Images Colour Library Ltd, page 25;
The Telegraph Colour Library, page 41.
All other photos by Trevor Clifford.
Title page: The Image Bank
Front cover: The Image Bank
Picture Research: Penni Bickle

PEARSON EDUCATION LIMITED
Edinburgh Gate, Harlow, Essex, CM20 2JE, England
and Associated Companies throughout the World.

First published 1995
Sixth impression 1999
ISBN 0 582 12240 6

Printed in Singapore (JBW)

The publisher's policy is to use paper manufactured from sustainable forests.

Windows

Hey, you down there
Yes, you my friend
I can see your cottage from my hotel window
I imagine your life as I look
Down at you, window to window
Daily you listen to the sea
And the black cat on your painted wall
Looks back at me.

Primrose Lockwood,
Hope Cove, South Devon, May 1993

A poem about housework

I'm the arranger
of landscapes on dishes:
dunes of potatoes
and forests of greens,
small lakes of ketchup
around fishcake islands,
red moons of tomatoes,
brown shingle of beans.

I am the dancer
of dances with dusters:
fresh-smelling sarabands
lavender-sweet.
Oh, the polishing polkas!
Floor-shining fandangoes!
Spray can in my hands
soft cloths tied round my feet.

I'm the one with the iron
smoothing out creases.
See how it hisses
and presses and steams!
I push the hot silver
through outcrops of denim.
The height of my bliss is
wrinkle-free dreams …

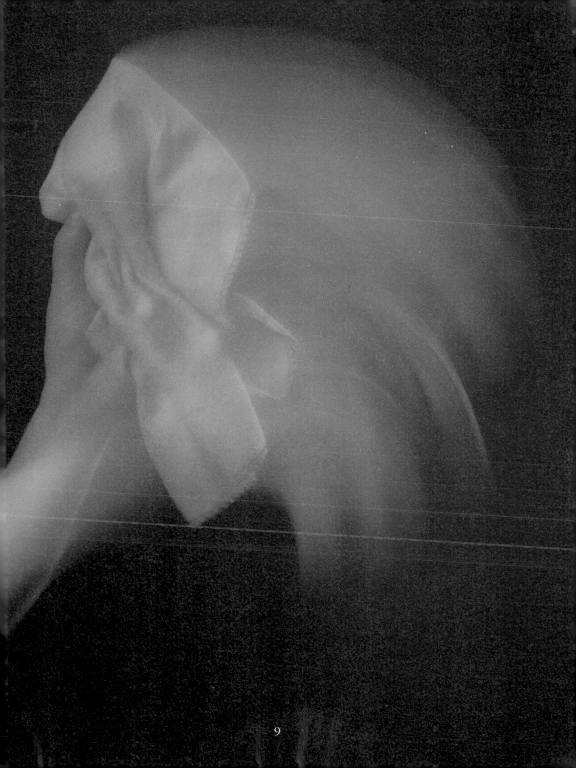

I lie on the sofa
composing this verse.
The state of my house
goes from bad to worse.

To write elegant lines is not my intention.
I regard poems as Housework Prevention.

Adèle Geras

Seaside

Once, in St. Anne's, the sea had slipped away
and soft, beige mud squeezed up between her toes.
"Where does the water go to when it goes?
And will it come again another day?"

She wanted sapphire waves that curled and spread
and stitched white frills of lace along the sand,
wanted to catch the water in her hand,
wanted to run and follow as it fled.

At last it dribbled in, dun-coloured, flat,
and then it turned and dribbled out again,
flattened and pock-marked by the thin, grey rain.
The sea was disappointing. That was that.

But in her dreams a turquoise ocean swells.
Three-masted clippers fly before the breeze.
Waking, she listens. Whispers from the seas
come to her, faintly, from collected shells.

Adèle Geras

Reasons for writing

Write when you are happy
and capture it to keep.
Write when you are sad
– it's better than a weep.

Write when you are angry,
to let the anger out.
You can note down all the things
that make you stamp and shout.

Write about the people you love
and watch the feeling grow;
as warm words touch paper,
see how they glow.

Perhaps you're missing someone
you've not seen for a while?
By writing about them,
your words can bring their smile.

When something funny happens,
that makes you laugh out loud,
write it and remember
to share it with a crowd.

If you feel a failure,
'cos you didn't win the cup,
you can write about it

and cheer the whole team up.
When night comes, and darkness
magnifies a fear,
write about what frightens you
and watch it disappear.

If, while asleep and dreaming,
you weave stories in your head,
don't forget to jot them down
– keep a pen beside the bed,

'cause it's a shame to waste ideas
or a special experience,
when you can fill a treasure chest
with your personal documents …

So when the world seems dull and dark
and you want to shed some light,
you know the way – it's easy –
just grab a pen and write!

Carolyn Askar

The Yeti

"Steep

Is the peak,

But we must keep

Watch for the beast we seek,

I'd give half my life for a peep

At the Yeti, the shaggy abominable freak

Who, I'm convinced, exists, for he steals the sheep

Of the Sherpas who live down the valley, by the creek."

After four months of searching our leader was ready to weep,

Tired, we encamped that night and since our prospects were bleak,

Reluctantly decided to pack up and leave after a good night's sleep,

But the next morning when we woke up, our heads swam and knees felt weak

To see all our luggage neatly packed and lying outside on the snow in a heap

With a note attached which said: "Good riddance, snooping monsters." What a cheek!

ebjani Chatterjee

Rocky

There's more to life than lying in the sun
For anyone who has a list of chores
Or something urgent waiting to be done.

You, on the other hand, can rest your paws,
Sleep in a patch of light, wake up and purr,
Use the settee for sharpening your claws

In your own time. Days merge, become a blur.
You have no sense of human haste, no plan,
Nothing to do but rearrange your fur.

Life's easy. There will be another can
Of cat food, or if not you'll catch some birds.
I envy you your short attention span.

Your refreshing lack of words.

Sophie Hannah

Gloves (poem for a Valentine card)

You won't find any hints
Enclosed, no cryptic clues, no fingerprints,

Nothing about the gender,
Background or occupation of the sender.

Anonymous, unseen –
You're dealing with the all-time king or queen

Of undercover loves,
The author of this Valentine wore gloves.

Sophie Hannah

Family meals

My grandma bakes
the oven glows warm and full
with pies and stews and cakes
that take their time.
Comfy, warm and slow,
smells drift and grow until
"Here you are, love."
The house is peaceful, warm and still.
My gran has the time.

My mum fries.
She fries and grills and boils.
Food sizzles and fizzes.
Steams, spits and hisses
and splatters like a greasy firework.
Then clatter BANG! "It's done!
Hurry up! Must run!"
Behind her the door shuts with a crash.
My mum has to dash.

My dad shrugs
His cupboard is bare.
"Everything I make goes up in smoke!"
He grins uneasily, tries to joke.
He buys me burgers – double cheese, large fries,
chocolate milkshake – giant size.
"Anything you want. O.K.?"
He ruffles my hair. "See you Sunday."
My dad goes away.

Michaela Morgan

Love hearts

Sweets for the sweet

February 14th
playing Cupid
girl on my table acting stupid
passing sweets to me

They say I Love You
and You're so Fine
my friends crease up at Please be Mine
She must have packets of them

All through maths they come
Great Guy
Don't Blush
Then Trust Me that kind of mush

It's really getting to me
Then Speak To Me
and Hold Me Tight
So at break I go up to her
All right!

She blinks at me
Her smile is growing
Offers a sweet

Be Kind is showing

I snatch them, push her
Run off crowing

All afternoon
I'm thinking how she felt
I smell the sweet and sickly scent
as pastel messages fizz and melt

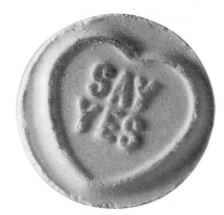

I send back Crazy! and No Chance
I nudge and snigger Wanna Dance?
I chuck No Way and flick Big Deal
I throw In Love and make her squeal

Then
When
All my friends have gone away
I quietly give her Don't Cry
and U R O K

Michaela Morgan

Blake's Tyger - revisited

On hearing that tigers in captivity can gradually lose their colour, losing
their camouflaging stripes and fading gradually to white.

Tiger! Tiger! Turning white
In a cage just twice your height
Six paces left, six paces right,
A long slow day, a longer night.

Tiger! Tiger! Dreaming still
Of the scene? The chase? the kill?
And now? No need. No place. No scope.
No space. No point. No hope.

Tiger! Tiger! Paces. Paces.
Once he flashed through open spaces
His world once echoed to his roars.
Now he's quiet. He stares. He snores.

An inch of sky glimpsed through the bars.
A puddle, concrete, smells of cars.
He sniffs the air. He slumps. He sighs.
And stares and stares through jaundiced eyes.

Michaela Morgan

I don't cry

Throat burns,
Eyes sting,
Face swells,
Reddening.

Nose sniffs,
Lips quake,
Chin trembles,
Legs shake.

Tears drop.

You what?
Crying?
Me! Cry!
Nah – I've just got something in my eye …

Michaela Morgan

Malham Tarn Field Centre - Yorkshire, 1992

The full moon stands above the tarn
And sees three moons reflected there;
Shadowy rabbits dance the sward,
The midges fidget in the air;
Across the lake a single note:
A curlew calls into the night.
The larches, dark on darkening air,
Are like a curtain drawn apart
To show the moon above the tarn
That sees three moons reflected there.

Gerda Mayer

The mermaids in the sea are

The mermaids in the sea are
Far hardier than we are,
And in the summer wear
Only the gilded air,
The blue translucencies
And foam-lace of the seas.
But when the seas are rough
They put on sailors' stuff:
Garments that seamen wore
Who never reached a shore.
They sit on rocks and crunch
An oceanic lunch.
They suck on bones and ribs,
They smack their salty lips
Above their sailor-bibs.

Gerda Mayer

Stock still

There was a woman who stood stock-still
in the middle of the street.
"Shall I go shopping today," she said,
"and buy some things to eat
for a treat
or shall I go home again," she said,
"and make do with whatever there is to be had?"

The shops they shut and opened again,
and shut and opened once more;
her husband came home and went out again,
and came back, and went out through the door.
And still the woman stood in the street
and went neither to nor fro.
"There's not much point in moving," she said,
"'Till I know which way to go."

So long she stood, so much engrossed,
she's turned into a sign-post.

Gerda Mayer

No ball games

No ball games, no bat games,
No "Caught out, owzat!" games.
The sign has just gone up and it says
No ball games.

No catching, no throwing
In case the grass stops growing
The park is just for looking at, so
No ball games.

It's hard if you're sport mad
No sense in getting caught, lad.
In winter they can't stop you playing
Snowball games!

Sue Cowling

**NO CYCLING
NO SKATEBOARDING
NO BALL GAMES
IN THIS AREA**

Pete's leg

Pirate Pete wore a wooden leg
On Monday he drummed with it on a rum keg
On Tuesday he used it to stir his stew
On Wednesday he lent it to a roosting cockatoo
On Thursday he learned how to make it dance
On Friday he rowed with it over to France
He sat in Calais on a fine Saturday
And said "Sunday tomorrow, I may as well stay."
The leg seemed to flourish in foreign air
And turned blue, white and red, which suited Pirate Pierre!

Sue Cowling

Night

Night is a deep forest,
snagging dream-time on its
outstretched branches.

Night fixes me with an
evil eye, snarls my feet in
great tangled roots.

Moonlight scribbles across
the shadows, highlights
a sense of loneliness

Like the last person left
on earth, I stumble from tree
to bone-bare tree.

Dreams lure me on to
dangerous pathways, tempt me
into sightlessness.

I tell beads of blackness;
sloe, raven, jet, ebony.
Bat-dark depths entice me.

I hear the moon-songs of
dying leaves, the night-cry
of mosses, stars sighing.

Moira Andrew

Poems aren't all that difficult

(For David)

Clothes whirled and twirled
like a merry-go-round, socks
and shorts, skirts and tops.

I stared into the eye of the
machine. "The clothes look
like melted colour," I said.

Mum was amazed. "My boy,"
she said, "You've made a poem."
I didn't know it was so easy.

Moira Andrew

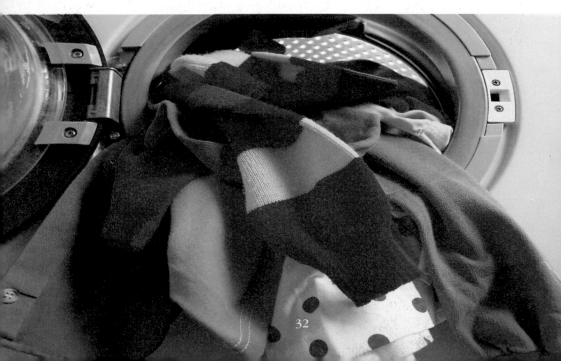

Nursery rhyme 1992

There was an old woman
who lived in a box.
She had so few possessions
she'd no need for locks.
They gave her some soup
with two slices of bread.
Then she wrapped up in rags,
made the pavement her bed.

Moira Andrew

Go-cart

We yanked the wheels
off Tansey's old black pram
and hammered them
to make our racing-cart:
its clattering struck
the tufts of summer grass
and shook
the dusty buttercups
going up the hill.

Then letting go
we knew the hectic thrill
of astronauts
who with one mighty shove
thrust from behind them
all that they know and love.

Una Leavy

Bells

Paula goes with Pop
to ring the bell,
startled she hears it
peal and swell
across the breeze
and down the sleepy streets.

He ties the rope
against the warm stone
and holds her hand.

Inside the aisle
is cool and blue and dim,
she trots with him
past polished pews until
they stop where daffodils
run frills of yellow
round the altar steps.

Years pass
and Paula follows Pop.
She hears
the tolling bell
and sees through tears
the daffodils all woven into wreaths.

Una Leavy

School reports

Potentially she is an able girl –
A friendly Junior, conduct fairly good.
If she'd exert herself, she could do well.

Class singing: Fair – she must learn to stand still.
Neatness and handwriting could be improved.
Potentially she is an able girl.

Avoids lacrosse whenever possible.
When she's admonished, she is sometimes rude.
If she'd exert herself, she could do well.

Her whole approach is far too casual –
She is erratic, work depends on mood.
Potentially she is an able girl.

She's growing up, is much more sensible.
Still talks too much and reads less than she should.
If she'd exert herself, she could do well.

As Head of House she's been reliable.
We wish her all the best in adulthood.
Potentially she is an able girl –
If she'd exert herself, she could do well.

Wendy Cope

Where do you get your ideas from?

They used to be delivered by the milkman –
"Two pints please and a brilliant idea" –
But they began to vanish from the doorstep
And I was only getting three a year.

I tried the shop – the big one down in Norwood,
I-D-R-Mart. I wandered down an aisle
Where Nature was displayed in great abundance,
Trees, flowers, sunsets, dead sheep (by the pile)

The usual stuff. I hurried past Domestic,
Domestic Pets (BE TENDER! MOURN YOUR CAT!),
And Politics (GREAT VALUE! EEZEE TARGETS!)
And paused at Love. But I was sick of that.

It's difficult. It's worse than buying trousers.
They have to be just right. They're hard to find.
No luck for weeks. Then someone asks a question
And gives me one I like. How very kind.

Wendy Cope

37

Fair game

Chrissie's taking the long way home –
Through a maze of streets and alleyways
She scurries, close to walls,
A little cringing ghost in a grey school uniform.
No-one sees her flitting by,
She blends in with the concrete and the rain-washed sky.

She yearns to be invisible –
For then, there'd be an end to running scared,
A rest from fear: "What's that?"
She's frantic as a hare that hears the baying hounds.
They must have tracked her down!
Stalked her, sniggering, through the back streets of the town.

For she's fair game to them–
Those three girls who make her life such misery.
An easy victim,
Uniting them in power and superiority:
"And it's real good fun!"
"I mean, how can you feel sorry for any kid that dumb … !"

But there's pain and dread in Chrissie's eyes
Deeper than you can measure
Like any gentle creature
Pursued for others' pleasure.

Susan Gates

All the way to Africa

It's two weeks now since Grandma died,
and I've found these cloths in her bottom drawer–
they came with her from Africa
forty years ago or more –
I shake them out and spread them on her bed.
And they're burning, flaming orange, red!
Screaming to be free
of this grey and dreary room. Aching
to be far away
in Africa
by a purple jacaranda tree.
Draping hips that sway
to the rhythm of the drum,
brushing feet
that stamp to the beat
in ochre dust.
Wait! I think I can hear the coiled bracelets clink
on black, oiled skin.
Even from this housing estate
drizzled in English rain,

I can taste the sugarcane!
These blazing colours take me there –
that scarlet glow, hot yellow
and wild electric blue.
Can you smell it too?
The roasting maize?
See that pink explosion of flamingoes
as they rise up from the surface of the lake
with a thunderous whirring of a thousand wings?
Now, I've never been to Africa –
But, oh, my Grandma told me things …
There's a noise outside – an ice-cream van
is tinkling "Popeye the Sailorman".
My daydream falls apart
I can't hear drumbeats anymore.
So I take the cloths and fold them,
and shut Africa away again
in Grandma's bottom drawer.

Susan Gates

Pearlie Mountblossom

Pearlie Mountblossom's lost her mother
she lives in a tent with her Dad and her brother,
the wind blew out and the tent blew in
and Pearlie early learned to swim,

Pearlie dreams in her tent at night
that the sails are set and the stars are bright
and the waves are turning over and over
and they show the face of Pearlie's mother,

Pearlie Mountblossom has forty pounds
she keeps it safe in a hole in the ground,
her leggings have stars on, her dreams are sweet
though her brother is snoring down by her feet,

Pearlie Mountblossom grows mustard seeds
she keeps her flowerpots clean of weeds,
her mustard blows in the morning wind
while Pearlie's father shaves and sings,

Pearlie has friends but they never come home,
her brother plays but he plays alone,
her Dad splits kindling to make the fire
and the flames leap higher and higher and
higher,

Pearlie Mountblossom's lost her mother
she lives in a tent with her Dad and her brother,
she has apples for breakfast and Mars Bars for tea
and at night she sails the whispering sea.

Helen Dunmore

Light as a leaf

Her boat was light as a leaf on her back
as she carried it to the shoreline,

there was a smudge of grey behind the huts –
she'd timed it well, it was dawn.

Her boat was light as a leaf
as she sat, chin on her knees

and felt the cold tide start to pull
at the frame of her coracle,

she was quick and neat as a fish
as she paddled away out of it,

out of the smoke, and the dogs barking,
and a winter of old people dying.

Her boat span like a leaf
in the rip-tide by the rocks

so by the time the sun came up
she and her coracle were a dot

as she sailed off somewhere
the story can't follow her.

Helen Dunmore

Jack's tale

"At day-break, Jack finding the Giant not likely to be soon roused,
crept softly out of his hiding-place, seized the hen, and ran off with her."

Iona & Peter Opie: The Classic Fair Tales

Sun rises before me,
dazzles pathless flight.
In the corner of each eye
mists drift and fade,
dissolve against a lightening sky;
the tops of oaks sprawl
like giant undergrowth below,
I dare not pause to gaze,
I dare not fall!

Behind, as if in smoke,
the castle disappears.
My life is ruled by noise:
heart drums inside my chest,
the giant thud of angry steps
invades my ears.

Beneath one arm
a squirming weight of feathers,
crooked between waist and elbow,
squawks our whereabouts into the dawn;
scratches tales of panic into flesh.
All thoughts are on escape:
all golden dreams have flown!
Ahead, at last,
green stalks emerge from cloud
then cobweb downwards,
stitching earth to sky.
I leap, grasp branches urgently
with outstretched hand; half-slide, half-fall
to blessed earth below,
to blessed land.

Judith Nicholls

A captured warrior waits to be sacrificed

Blow, blow the sacred conch,
beat the great drum for me,
sound the sacred fluting pipes
in the still, morning air.

The music reaches through the carved stones
of my prison, warming my cold limbs,
on the day of my death.

Sun, Sun, I must give my heart,
spill for you my warrior blood
to nourish you, oh Huitzilpochtli
in your battle with the night.

I can hear the priests far off
sounding their sacred music as the sun rises
on the day of my death.

Sound the sacred, fluting pipes
in the still, morning air,
Sun, Sun, I must give my heart,
spill for you my warrior blood.

When they come to take me into the light,
oh Huitzilpochtli, fill me with courage
on the day of my death.

As my heart beats on the altar
and I leave this world to join the gods
blow, blow the sacred conch,
beat the great drum for me.

Heather Eyles

A Spanish soldier first sees Tenochtitlan

Such a long journey we had
in the heat and the flies
and the deaths on the way.
So much blood we left behind us
in the jungle where the jaguar prowls.

But we pressed on for God
and for Spain. There was no going back
even had we wanted to,
for our ships were burnt behind us,
torched by our General
to encourage those less valiant of heart.

Such a long climbing ever upward
on foot and on horseback, our bodies,
our beards, itching in the heat,
stumbling over stones, not knowing
what we would find, if anything.

And we found this.

As we rounded the pass
between the two mountains, our eyes
red-rimmed, our clothes filled with dust,
the light of the great lake smote our faces
and temples and causeways magnificent
rose before us. The most beautiful city

ever seen in all the world.
Our hearts leapt at the sight
of its wondrous treasures.

We thought of all the glory
we would win for our King
and all that we would take
for ourselves.

Heather Eyles

There's a surprise

There's a surprise
waiting for you
in this box.

It's every colour
some tastes
most sounds
a lot of sniffs
and it feels
like sandpaper.

All you have to do
is open it.
Here's the key.

It's a day of the week
a leaf
a picture book

or it's a fight
a sickness
a loss.

Here's the key.

Sue Stewart

February

I taste of ice before snowdrop,
of a storm in a teacup.

I ruffle your hair in play,
polish your cheeks to a cold red.

Breath me in, it's the only way
to test me. Will I sting or sooth?

I speak to you of Valentine
though my own heart is cold.

All you see are bare branches,
but the sap rises like a secret.

I walk in slow motion,
preparing for the race.
I start off in second place.

Sue Stewart

Shadow

I saw a shadow
talking to itself
a long time ago

shaking its head
as if what it heard
wasn't what it said

laughing
at the same time
as crying

then it saw me
and opened its wings
like a moth, and flew off.

Sue Stewart

Wheels-song

I don't know why I've got feet
when I could have had wheels,
for wheels go so much faster.

Imagine me flying down our street
not in my trainers or boots
but on wheels, with my ghetto-blaster.

Imagine people turning to stare,
and all telling me to slow down
before I caused a disaster.

Imagine me gliding off into space
with a brief sure nod to the Moon,
then simply going straight past her.

Imagine ...

Katherine Gallagher

Sylvester Snake

Sylvester Snake
started to shake,
he knew the signs
of a huge earthquake.

"Let's fly", he said
to the other snakes,
"it's no place for us
when the ground gets the shakes."

So he led them
hissing fast and free
over mountains and streams
to a Snake-Jamboree.

There were black and brown snakes,
copperheads galore,
tiger-snakes and taipans
and many, many more …

They danced and hissed
to the music of the flute;
Sylvester did gymnastics
and ate a passion-fruit –

then slung himself a hammock
between two trees,
and dozed off to music
from a band of bumblebees.

Katherine Gallagher

Books

Our house is chock-a-block
with books. This is crazy –

it's impossible to read them all
but they're part of the family.

Sometimes when I'm hunting out a title,
I find one I'd forgotten.

We greet like old friends – then
I forget what I was searching for.

There's a lot of forgetting
when it comes to books,

Occasionally I discover one
I've forgotten to give back.

Oh dear ... If one day
I can't be found, I expect

I'll be somewhere in the house –
squeezed between the covers of a book.

Katherine Gallagher